OTHER BOOKS BY WALT KELLY

TEN EVER-LOVIN' BLUE-EYED YEARS WITH POGO

PREHYSTERICAL POGO
THE POGO POOP BOOK
THE RETURN OF POGO
DECK US ALL WITH BOSTON CHARLIE
POGO PUCE STAMP CATALOG

INSTANT POGO	THE POGO PARTY
GONE POGO	THE POGO SUNDAY BOOK
POGO À LA SUNDAE	POTLUCK POGO
POGO EXTRA	POGO PEEK-A-BOOK
BEAU POGO	THE INCOMPLEAT POGO
THE POGO SUNDAY BRUNCH	THE POGO STEPMOTHER GOOSE
G. O. FIZZICKLE POGO	THE POGO PAPERS
THE POGO SUNDAY PARADE	UNCLE POGO SO-SO STORIES
POSITIVELY POGO	I GO POGO
POGO'S SUNDAY PUNCH	POGO

* * *

SONGS OF THE POGO   POGOMOBILE

* * *

In collaboration with Pogo
THE JACK ACID SOCIETY BLACK BOOK

WALT KELLY

SIMON AND SCHUSTER
New York

Published by Simon and Schuster
Rockefeller Center, 630 Fifth Avenue
New York, New York 10020

Library of Congress Catalog Card Number: 68-8583
Manufactured in the United States of America

4 5 6 7 8 9 10 11 12 13 14 15

Contents

For
Miss Florence Blackham
who for a hundred years
has had equal time for
everybody . . .
1968

*As we pursued our peace in queues this past year, many of us turned over stone images only to have them turn upon us. This is the nature of revolution.

Nature abhors a vacuum, and as one vacuum after another dropped out of the race recently, Nature, in compulsive revolution, hastily threw another vacuum into the breach.

About page 36 of this book, Romney, his mouth full of early foot, decided to drop the pretense of running. He was honest, an expensive trait. At the time it was thought that he had set a trend. The nobility of the act was so appealing that others emulated the move. But they had the bad grace to lurk in worried ambivalence. All this to-and-fro work causes a cartoonist, who works in the presumption of ordinary incongruity for the future book, to throw up his hands. One plays it safe then, and bets on a Sure Thing.

By page 51 (April Fool's Day Eve), the Sure Thing dropped. No saliva test was necessary.

Previously (page 49), a national newspaper thought it detected a Familiar Resemblance in the POGO strip of March 21. Quivering with courage, it dropped all future uses of the caricature. It was declared that such use was beneath its dignity. It was not beneath its dignity on March 11 and 12 (page 40), or maybe nobody on the staff reads his own newspaper.

After that there was not much to do except offer alternate strips for such days as people left their feelings lying around loose. These strips are identifiable by the letter A added after the date in the first panel. None of the damaging, dastard strips of the same date bears the letter A.

It must be admitted that Nature precedes comic art. As we thrash on to a finish through the current thicket of flags and banners, we realize it is no finish at all, but a new inning. Secure in the rules, we know that, given three strikes, the truth will out.†

W. K., 1968

†*footnote to a footnote:* The cartooned figure of Senator Robert can be found here. Normally the cartoonist drops the caricature of one who has departed. But, in truth, it is hard to comprehend that this friend is gone. Besides, he believed in the fun we all have shared. To that extent also, he lives on.

Chapter 1

THE PAST PARDISCIPLE OF THE PRESENT TENSION

ARE YOU A CANDIDATE, MR. PRESIDENT... I MEAN, MR. CONGERSMAN ?
I cannot now prognosticate Just Whom will be the Candidate Nor whom will be my Running Mate....
DUNNO WHAT'S WRONG, CHIEF, BUT SOME LI'L' THING THERE SEEMS TO MAKE YOUR INTENTION TOO CLEAR.
WHICH WAY?
FEEBLE E. MERELY, CHANGE MY DISAVOWAL SPEECH ABOUT MY...UH ... THE CANDIDENTURE FOR THE PRESIDENSITY SO IT MAKES A BETTER COVER UP...
RIGHT, BOSS.
11-7
MAKE IT LOOK LIKE I'M VERY RELUCTANTLY REJECTIONABLE, THO' WILLING IF DRAFTED.
HERE'S WHAT YOU HAD: "I cannot now prognosticate Just whom will be the Candidate Nor whom will be my Running mate."
YOU CHANGED THAT TO: "Whomever is the Candidate, I'll never be my Running Mate..."
BETTER, HUH?
BETTER!? YOU CLOWN! YOU GOT ME TALKIN' MYSELF OUT OF BOTH TOP SPOTS, MERELY.
MY PHILES!

CONGERSMAN FENSTER MOOP AS I LIVE AN' BREATHE! AN' FEEBLE E. MERELY!
POGO, LET US SING YOU MY DISAVOWAL SPEECH.
11-9
SING? DISAVOWAL SPEECH?
YEH, OL' BUDDY, I'M MAKIN' A SWEEP TO LAND AN OPINION ON WHETHER I SHOULD RUN FOR PRESIDENT.
SING IT, MAN.
LAND'N OPINION? YOU 'MEMBER WHAT THAT DID FOR THE LITERAL DIGEST IN 19 AN '36?
WE CALL IT THE PULSE POLL.
I'LL SING. OOMPH, OMP OMPH OMPA OOMPH!
IN NEW YORK MR. MERELY WOULD BE COLLARED FOR VIOLATIN' THE SULLIVAN ACT.
RIGHT, OL' BUDDY, MERELY CARRIES A TUNE LIKE IT WAS A CONCEALED WEAPON.
WHO'S SINGIN'? THIS IS JES' ONLY THE VAMP. OOMPH OMPH ORNK OOMPA OMP
MY DISAVOWAL SPEECH GOTTA SHOW I IS MODEST AN' SELF EFFACIN' SO'S FOLKS'LL THINK I'M PUTTIN' ON THE SHUCKS ABOUT BEIN' PRESIDENT.
Y'CAN'T PAINT YER-SELF INTO A CLOSET, THO'.
mi mi mi mi mi mi mi
11-10
THERE HE GO WITH MY DISAVOWAL NOW.
Tho' I'm not now a Candidate, I really must reiterate I have in mind my running mate.... Who must bestir his addled pate.

Astutely, stoutly, strongly state He'll maybe join the proper slate And, holding back, not hesitate To random ride our tandem fate....
HE GOT VIM!
VIM! ONE TIME, IN A HA' PENNY TENT OPERA, HE SUNG SUCH A FIERY, BANG-BANG, HARUM SCARUM, DRAG 'EM OUT DEATH SCENE, I DIN'T THINK HE'D LIVE THROUGH IT.
OOMP WUMP OOMPH!
CONGERSMAN MOOP... DEACON MUSHRAT SAY THE WAY TO DEAL WITH THE ENEMY IS ON HIS OWN TERRITORY!
I AGREE!
11-16
I PROMISE, WHEN ELECTED, TO GO OVERSEAS AND SETTLE EVERYTHING.
YOU PROMISED A LOT TO BE ELECTED CONGERSMAN, TOO.
YOU DELIVERED ZERO OR LESS.
WELL, WELL! NOT EVERYONE'S PERFECT YOU KNOW... YOU DON'T ELECT A GOD, Y'KNOW.
DEPENDS...
...WHICH PARTY?

Chapter 2

OUT OF THE MOUTHS OF BABES AND CANNONS

IF YOU WIND UP WITH A GOD FOR, LIKE, SAY PRESIDENT, WHOSE FAULT IS THAT? HIS OR THEM AS VOTES FOR HIM?
WHAT'S THAT?
YEH, WHAT IS THAT?
WHAT WE MAYBE OUGHT TO DO, POGO, IS HAVE A SANITY TEST FOR VOTERS.
HOW COME, CONGERSMAN?
WE WANT TO GIVE FOLKS A BRAIN PROBE TO CARRY A GUN, TO DRIVE A CAR.
11-22
BUT FOR THE MOST RISKY THING OF ALL, CHOOSIN' A PRESIDENT, WE LET ANYBODY OVER 21 GO IN THERE AN' LAY THE COUNTRY ON THE LINE...
WE COULD CHANGE THE CONSTITUTION, NOBODY OVER 21 CAN VOTE.
BULLY! GETS RID OF ALL THEM NUTTY PEOPLE OVER 21.
TROUBLE IS ALL THE NUTS AIN'T NECESSARILY ADULTS.

WHAT IS THIS HERE, DEACON, A 1968 MODEL TORQUE-MADA?
No, me an' Mole is testing the cannon.
D'YOU S'POSE IF ONLY FOLKS UNDER 21 IS ALLOWED TO VOTE THAT THEY WOULD VOTE FOR ANYBODY WHO CALL HISSELF A GOD.
HARD TO SAY..... MAYBE... IF THEY BELIEVE IN ANY...
11-23

LOOK LIKE OL' MOLE IS STUCK.
In a pig's neck he's stuck!
NO, IN A CANNON, IN A CAVERN, I'M STUCK.
11-24

GOT 'IM!

THANKS.. ...UH, EXCUSE ME, GENTS.

FORGOT MY HAT....
THERE'S A LESSON HERE SOMEWHERE, POGO, SON.

Chapter 3

THE SQUARE PIG IN A ROUND WORLD

WHEN YOU SAYS YOU GOT A SANITY CLAUSE IN YO' PLATFORM, CONGERSMAN PROG, IS THIS THE FELLA WITH THE BAG? THE BAG MAN?
YEH, LIKE HE COME DOWN THE CHIMBLEY? LOTSA PARTIES OFFER THAT CLAUS REAL CONSTANT.
NO-- THIS IS A SANITY CLAUSE TO SEE IF THE VOTER IS SANE--- IN THE BRAIN, Y'KNOW.
12-9

Y'GONNA EXAMINE THE VOTER FOR THIS?

WHO GONNA EXAMINE THE CANDIDATE?
WELL, NOW! IF HE AIN'T A VOTER, HE'S HOME FREE, RIGHT?

YOU REALLY MEAN THAT YO' PLATFORM GONNA HAVE A SANITY CLAUSE IN IT?
ONE HUNDRED POOR CENT.
12-11

SANITY CLAUSE? YOU SURE YOU DON'T MEAN A GIVE-AWAY PROGRAM?
NO, THEM IS OLD HAT--- NOTHIN' NEW THERE-- WE EVEN GOT TWO OF 'EM.

ONE BEIN' A OVERSEAS PROJECK AN' THE OTHER GIVE-AWAY BEIN' WHEN YOUR NEIGHBOR GIVES YOU AWAY TO THE TAX MAN FOR CONCEALIN' INCOME.
S.S. OL' BILL
SO THIS SANITY CLAUSE INVOLVES THE VOTER PROVIN' HE'S SANE? WHAT ABOUT THE CANDIDATE?
IN TIMES LIKE THESE, HOW WOULD IT LOOK FOR A CANDIDATE TO GO 'ROUND TRYIN' TO PROVE HE'S NOT INSANE?
TOP DRAWER
THE HON. BILL GALLO
CONGERSMAN FROG CLAIM HIS SANITY CLAUSE WON'T REQUIRE THE CANDIDATE TO PROVE HE'S SANE.
JES' THE VOTER? WELL, MEBBE THAT'S BEST.
FORT MUDGE
12-12
MEBBE... THE CANDIDATE MIGHT BE MORE ATTRACTIVE IF HE COULD PROVE HIMSELF INSANE -- TO BE SANE IN AN INSANE WORLD WOULD BE INCONGRUOUS.
IN CONGRUOUS ASSEMBLED, THEREFORE, WE AFFIRM THE WORLD IS INSANE AN' WILL ELECT A NUTTY LEADER TO COPE WITH IT! THEREBY GIVIN' HIM AN OUT!
AN OUT?
SURE .. NO MATTER WHAT HE DOES HE CAN BE PROVEN INNOCENT BY REASON OF INSANITY.
INNOCENT BY REASON OF INSANITY?

DID YOU SEE HOW MUCH LIVIN' COSTS HAVE GONE UP?... THE BIGGEST INCREASE IS IN HOUSING AN' TAXES.
HEY! FRIDAY, THE THIRTEENTH, COME ON WEN'S DAY... SO WE'RE SAFE, I SAYS.
WAYCROSS
12-13
AN' I SAYS HOUSING AN' TAXES COMPRISE THE BIGGEST INCREASES IN LIVING COSTS.
SEE!? SPENDIN' FOR FRIPPERIES! IT ALWAYS SHOWS! LUXURIES! IT'LL RUIN US ALL!
LUXURIES?
DANG RIGHT! TAXES! WHO NEEDS 'EM?
HOW CAN YOU STAND THERE AN' CLAIM TAXES SHOULD BE DONE AWAY WITH?
WHO'S STANDIN'? I'M LYIN'....
12-14
PROB'LY TRUE...
THERE'S BETTER THINGS TO SPEND OUR MONEY ON THAN TAXES... ALL THEM BILLIONS FOR WHAT?

Chapter 4

DEAD WRONG BY RIGHTS

ALL YOUR TALK ABOUT ME GOIN' ON A DIET IS MAKIN' ME STARVE.. I DECLARE LUNCHTIME.
RESOLUTIONS
1-11
ALONG WITH THIS RESOLUTION I WRIT FOR YOU TO LOSE TEN LBS. GOES A EXTRA SERVICE AT NO AD'L CH'GE...
EG, IE, ETC?
SNOP!
WHILST YOU IS IN THE THROES OF THIS DIET, I'LL BE YOUR MGR.
F'G'T IT.. YRS TR'LY, G'BYE.
WE COME OVER ON A MATTER OF GRAVE IMPORT..
I KNOW.. FRIDAY, THE THIRTEENTH, COME ON SATURDAY.
1-12
WULL..WE'S SAFE ANYWAYS..OL' OWL HERE IS MY MANAGER ON A DIET I IS RUNNIN'.. HE SAY I GOTTA LOSE 10 POUNDS.
TEN?....C'MON INSIDE.

FISH
FRESH .20
OTHER .02
APPLES
10¢
QUART
THEM'LL RUN YE @ THUTTY CENTS PER QUART, MR. LAFEMME.
MIGGLE'S
AAH, YOU FALSE FRIEND! TELLIN' ME I GOTTA LOSE TEN POUNDS.
1-15
THEN POGO PROVES I ONLY WEIGH NINE.
MEANIN' I'D WIND UP WEIGHIN' MINUS ONE LB!
ONLY ONE SOLUTION THEN --- TO LOSE TEN POUNDS ON YOUR WEIGHT REDUCIN' DIET, YOU FIRST GOTTA GAIN 'BOUT A DOZEN.

Chapter 5

FUN RAISIN PIE

I NEVER BEEN SO INSULTED IN ALL MY LIFE... OWL PUT ME ON A DIET OF DRIED APPLES AN' WATER!
HUH?
1-18
DRIED APPLES AN' WATER WILL SWOLE YOU UP LIKE A DIRIGIBLE.
EXACTLY! HE GOTTA GO ON A REDUCIN' DIET TO LOSE TEN LBS BUT HE ONLY WEIGH NINE.
SO TO LOSE TEN HE GOTTA GAIN 'BOUT TEN?
AT LEAST.
IF I DON'T GET BETTER GRUB FROM YOU, THE MGR. OF MY DIET, I'M GOIN' ON A HUNGER STRIKE!
A VIOLATION OF CONTRACK! YOU GOTTA GAIN ON YOUR REDUCIN' DIET.. AN' A HUNGER STRIKE IS A WILDCAT MOVE...
THREATENIN' TO GO ON A HUNGER STRIKE 'STEAD OF A REDUCIN' DIET, WHAT NERVE!
NEMMINE, POGO LEF' ME HIS LUNCH,... GOOD, TOO.
1-19
BOYS, I DECIDED TO RUN A BIG FUND RAISING DINNER FOR THE CAMPAIGN SURGE.

THE CAMPAIGN SERGE? YOU EXPECK US TO COUNTERBUTE TO A NEW SUIT?
NOW NOW.. THE CONGERSMAN ONLY GOT OUR BEST INTER'STS AT HEART.
RIGHT!
WHAT'S WRONG WITH A FUN RAISIN' DINNER? HAVE SOME LUNCH, CONGERSMAN?
THANKS JUS' THE SAME 'BOUT LUNCH... I ALREADY IS ET-- WHERE'S MR. MERELY?
WASN'T MUCH LEFT ANYHOOS BY THE HEFT OF IT.
1-22
I DON'T SEE WHY YOU NEED A FUND RAISIN' DINNER TO BUY A NEW BLUE SERGE FOR YOUR CAMPAIGN!
NOT WHAT I SAID! I SAID FOR THE CAMPAIGN SURGE!
BWAMP!
A BIG POLITICAL ASSASSINATION!
GET ME MR. MERELY... I GOTTA DICTATE A BIG DYIN' STATEMENT.
MR. MERELY! .... OOH, HELLO THERE.

YOU DON'T LOOK SO MUCH LIKE YOU'RE DYIN'... YOU DON'T EVEN LOOK DEAD.
I BEEN THRU THIS BEFORE, DON'T JUDGE A BOOK BY ITS COVER.
IT'S ME, FEEBLE E. MERELY, SIR, HERE TO TAKE YOUR DYIN' STATEMENT.
1-23
OKAY, TAKE THIS, MERELY; TO WHOM IT MAY CONCERN: WITH MY DYING BREATH I REAFFIRM....
HOW DO YOU SPELL THAT TOOHOOMIT, SIR?
LISTEN, MERELY, CAN THE DELAY! I'M GOIN' FAST--TAKE THIS! WITH MY DYING BREATH I REAFFIRM AND REITERATE-- --GOT THAT?
HOLD IT, SIR! GOT A PENCIL, ANYBODY?
PROCEED SIR-- FOUND MY FOUNTAIN PEN-- GOT A PIECE PAPER, CHURCHY?
MERELY, IN A MINUTE THERE'S GONNA BE A CROWD PLEASIN' DEATH SCENE HERE WHAT'S GONNA FEATURE A SURPRISE GUEST STAR!
BY GOLLY, MAYBE YOU IS DYIN' THIS TIME, SIR... YOU GOT A RASH OF EYEBALLS ALL OVER.
THAT'S THE SPLASH FROM YOUR DAG NAB FOUNTAIN PEN!
AS A DYIN' MAN, I'D LIKE TO CONTINUE MY DYIN' STATEMENT--I STAND BEFORE YOU, CUT DOWN AS I WAS ABOUT TO FIGHT THE GOOD FIGHT FOR PUBLIC OFFICE.
1-24

BUT NEITHER STORM NOR DEATH NOR GLOOM OF NIGHT CAN STAY MY HAND! I SHALL RUN! I SHALL RUN NATHELESS!
WHO'S THIS NATHELESS, SIR?
A SUBSTITUTE! HOW CAN WE RUN A DEAD CANDIDATE?
WHAT'S THE DIFFERMINTS? WE VOTES THE ROSTER THAT WAY, FAIR OFT, ISN'T IT?
READ THAT BACK.
HOW LONG YOU GONE BE WITH US?
I STILL DON'T THINK YOU LOOKS AS DEAD AS YOU COULD, CONGERSMAN.
I GOT HIS DYIN' STATEMENT.. I'M GONNA GIVE IT TO THE PRESS.
DON'T RUSH... HE MAY HAVE A FEW REWRITES AFORE HE GOES TO HIS REWARD.
STICK AROUND, BABY.
1-25
DON'T JUDGE A BOOK BY ITS COVER, I ALWAYS SAYS.
WHAT IS YOUR COVER?
HIS COVER, UP TO NOW, HAS BEEN THAT HE AIN'T RUNNIN' BUT HE GOT HIS V.P. ALL PICKED.
MY DYIN' STATEMENT NOW INDICATES I IS RUNNIN'...
I STAND ON MY RECORD.
A PERFECK TYPE RECORD FOR A DEAD CANDIDATE, CONGERSMAN.

Chapter 6

WRINGING THE WRONG ON THE RIGHT RUNG

THESE DANG INK SPOTS WON'T GO AWAY.
LOOK LIKE YOU GOT 'BOUT FORTY DOZEN EYEBALLS, CONGERSMAN.
1-27
HARD TO SAY JUST WHERE YOU'RE LOOKIN'.. BUT, LEASTWISE ...
WHEN A CONSTITUENT SAYS, "LOOK ME IN THE EYE WHEN YOU SAY THAT...!"
YOU WON'T HAVE THE USUAL POLITICAL PROBLEM.
GREAT NEWS! GREAT NEWS! IS YOU THROUGH DYIN' YET?
VERY CLOSE, MY BOY... I'M BREATHIN' CAREFUL.
1-29
I TOLE THE THREE BATS ABOUT YOUR FUN RAISIN' DINNER --- I PUT 'EM DOWN FOR MORE'N $100 PER PIECE.
BULLY.

GO BACK AN' PUSH 'EM UP TO $500 EVEN EACH... MAN! THEM GUYS MUST BE LOADED!
NO... I SUSPECT THEY IS AS SOBER AS A JUDGE...
ALTHOUGH, OLD JUDGE SAM STARTS MAKIN' THE STUFF IN THE CELLAR AND FINISHES IT OFF ON THE WAY UPSTAIRS.
I'M SURE GLAD YOU CHAPS WANTS TO PARTICIPATE IN THE FUN RAISIN' DINNER! I'M PUTTIN' YOU DOWN FOR $500 A-PIECE.
FOR THAT KINDA DOUGH WE IS SUPER PARTICIPATRIOTS.
1-30
WITH THAT KINDA SPIRIT, I'M SURE CONGERSMAN MOOP WOULD BE HAPPY TO PUT YOU DOWN FOR TIME-AND-A-HALF.
$750! SPLENDID!
YOU PARTICIPATRIOTS KNOWS THE KEYSTONE OF THE CONGERSMAN'S PLATFORM IS HIS NEW SANITY CLAUSE!
IT FIGGERS.
BUT IS IT NEW?

Chapter 7

THE AMERICAN BOOTY ROSE

THERE'S SOMETHIN' WRONG HERE, MR. MERELY.
YOU GOT "CAMPAIGN" SPELLED ALL SOUR, CONGERSMAN.
FROGGY BOTTOM CAMPANE HQTRS
2-19
LOOKIN' AT IT YOUR WAY, YOU'RE RIGHT.
WRONG KINDA PANE.
FROGGY BUTTOM CAMPANE HQTRS
HOW'S THAT?
IT'S STILL THE WRONG KINDA PAIN.
FROGGY BUTTOM CAMPAIN
FER THE KIND OF ACTIVITY YOU'RE CONTEMPLATIN', MR. CONGERSMAN, THAT KINDA PAIN IS 'BOUT RIGHT.
MR. CONGERSMAN, P.T. BRIDGEPORT GOT ME SIGNED UP AS ADVANCE MAN FOR HIS WORLD BEATIN' CIRCUS.
BULLY!
2-20
WE OPEN IN NEW HAMPSHIRE.. INTERESTED IN THE CENTER RING?
MAN! PUT HER THERE..! US FROGS GOTTA STICK TOGETHER!

`COURSE, I'M NOT EXACTLY A FROG.
MMM--- TRUE!.. BUT YOU CAN LIVE THAT DOWN.
IN MY HEART YOU'LL ALWAYS HAVE THE HEART OF A FROG.
Y'KNOW THEY DIN'T GIVE OUT NO PEACE PRIZE LAST YEAR... IF YOU GOT THAT YOU'D BE A SHOO-IN.
RIGHT!
AND I DESERVE IT... AS A FAR SEEIN' CONGERSMAN I FOUGHT TOOTH AN' CLAW AGAINST THAT TOMPKINS GULF RESOLUTION IN `SIXTY-FOUR.
2-22
Y'SAY YOU VOTED AGAINST THE WAR GAMES, CONGERSMAN?
TO CLARIFY THE RECORD, SIR, I SAID I FOUGHT LIKE A TIGER VERSUS WAR GAMES.
SAME THING AIN'T IT?
NO--- I THEN DID MY BIT, I VOTED FOR 'EM.
2-23

BUT NOW, I, COURAGEOUSLY, COME OUT AND BRAVELY SAY I WAS HOODWINKED, SOFT-SOAPED, LAUNDERED!
MAN! WHAT CLEAR-EYED, SPARKLING SPUNK!
I DON'T SEE WHY WE CAN'T GET THE PEACE PRIZE FOR YOU ON THEM GROUNDS ALONE!
FOR THAT KINDA DOUGH I'LL SAY TWICE AS MUCH, TWICE AS BRAVE.
WHAT NEWS! POGO!
I B'LEEVE I CAN GET THE PEACE PRIZE FOR OL' CONGERSMAN FROG.
THE NOBEL PEACE PRIZE?
YEP... MY COUSIN WHAT RUNS NOBLE'S GROCERY GIVES AWAY A TURKEY EVERY YEAR FOR THE BEST COUNTERBUTION TO PEACE.
WHAT'S OL' FROG'S COUNTER-BUTION?
2-26

HE CHANGED HIS MIND--NOW HE WOULD VOTE AGAINST WAR--- THAT'S BRAVE, MAN.
WHO'S THIS GUY NOBLE?
MY COUSIN IGNATZ--- WE CALL HIM IG.
IG? THE IG NOBLE PEACE PRIZE?
OL' MOUSE IS ADVANCE MAN FOR P.T. WITH THE CIRCUS WHAT OPENS IN N. HAMPSHIRE.
FIGGERS
SOAP
3-1
HE GONNA GIT OL' CONGERSMAN FROG INTO THE CENTER RING...
FIGGERS
BY GITTIN' HIM THE LOCAL NOBLE PEACE PRIZE FOR BRAVERY IN CHANGIN' HIS MIND.
FIGGERS
THE PRIZE IS GIVEN BY MOUSE'S COUSIN, IGNATZ, GO BY NAME, IG. --SO THE CONGERSMAN GETS THE IG NOBLE PEACE PRIZE.
FIGGERS

Chapter 8

DON'T CAST YOUR MOLD IN WATER

YOU think THIS Model TALKS too MUCH, POGO?
WELL, MEBBE IT COULD JUST WALK, IF NOT RUN.
NEW HAMPSHIRE OR BUST
WIND-UP TOYS
3-5
It's got a built-in trick.... ! STARTS TO TALK--Presto!! It puts its FOOT IN MOUTH!!
(Watch Closely)
AHEM
WELL, YOU get the IDEA, OLD Chap?
AND FURTHERMORE--
HERE'S A OLD FAVORITE Model.. POGO
GOOD...I SEE THIS ONE DON'T NEED TO BE WOUND UP...I JES' SET IT DOWN.
NO WIND-UP
WIND-UP TOYS
3-6

Should of WARNED YOU!! OLD CHAP! THAT MODEL runs at the DROP of a HAT!
SHOULDA KEPT MINE ON.
NEW HAMPSHIRE OR BUST
NOW I make a CAT'S Cradle AND you PLACE YON WIND-UP TOY on The STRANDS!
WIND-UP TOYS
3-7
IT DANCES ON A TIGHT-ROPE! AND IT SINGS!
I'm a lady-in-waiting, I'm anticipating, A-waiting, a-waiting A sure paradox...
And ne'er have I seen a Sweeter or keener Or cuter or cleaner Or more fairer fox...
BOY! THAT'S CUTE!
CUTE as A BUTTON!! ACUTELY CUTE and cunning!!

This is WHAT I call OUR PUNCH LINE It ALSO sings!
PUNCH LINE WIND-UP TOYS
3-8
And if we once a Gala had,
A Gala Party now in sad
Flight from Sureness,
Pugned with Pureness,
Was Nobleness a shallow fad?

THANK YOU, my MULTITUDINOUS friends; THIS is a RIOTOUS send-off--A HAPPY AUGURY!
TRAVEL S.O.P. SAME OLD PARTY LINE
SOP
NEW HAMPSHIRE OR BURST
3-9

FORGOT TO TELL YOU... THE PLATFORM HAR'LY EVER GOES WITH THE OLD PARTY LINE.
MY WORD!
YOU'RE NEW?
NO, I'M JUST OF A DIFFERENT STRIPE THIS SEASON.
SAME OLD PARTY LINE
NEW HAMPSHIRE OR BUST

Chapter 9

NEED IT LIKE YOUR HEAD IN A HOLE

I'LL GET YOU OUT OF THERE CLEAN AS A WHISTLE.
EASY, OL' BUDDY... YOU'RE NOT GONNA SHORT-HORN YOUR OL' BUDDY?
3-12
NO, I'LL SAW THE SCENERY.
YOU DIN'T GO TO NEW HAMPSHIRE?
ABSENCE NOTED?
YESSUH!.... Underneath the jolly tree stood a photograph of Me, And a Bust, the very essence, Of the Absent Xmas Presence...
HOW'D HE GET HIS HEAD IN IN THE FIRST PLACE?
WURF

KNOW WHAT TODAY IS?
THE MORNIN' AFTER--- THE CIRCUS IS A-COMIN' BACK FROM NEW HAMPSHIRE.
3-13
FRIDAY, THE 13th, COME ON WENSDAY.
LOOKY THERE! THE FIRST ONE BACK. AN ACTOR IN THE SIDESHOW COMPANY.
HAIL! HI YO! YIPPEE!
THE POSTLUDE TO YESTERDAY IS THE PRELUDE TO TOMORROW.
ISN'T IT RE-MARKABLE HOW THAT GUY CAN TALK WITH NO HEAD?
NOT SPECIALLY... THE DOG IS A VENTRIL-OQUIST.
HEY! POGO!

COME ON, POGO.... I REPAIRED MY MOUNTAIN. LEMME TRY IT OUT WITH A FREE SHOT OF YOU.
CAMPAIGN FOTOS = CHEAP
SOUVENIR OF MT. RUSHMORE
3-14
DO YOU SEE WHAT I SEE? POGO'S BEING ENSHRINED! HE HAS BEEN CHOSEN!
The Candidate!
SAY CHEESE.
WHAT KIND?

HE'S ONE OF THE MIGHTY ON MOUNT RUSHMORE! A FUTURE FOREFATHER!
Eh?

WELL, WELL, LET ME BE THE FIRST TO CONGRATULATE YOU, MR. CANDIDATE!
HUH?
3-15
ONE THING YOU GOTTA DO... SHOW YOU'RE BETTER'N ANY-BODY AT FLYIN' A KITE
YOU CRAWL INTO THE MORTAR WITH THE CANNON BALL.... HANG ON TO THE CHAIN AND (BLAM!) WE SHOW THEM THAT...
YOU CAN FLY A CANNON BALL, --- HUH?
How can the Candidate flee in the face of such of a Opportunity?
STOP THE CANDIDATE!

HOW CAN YOU SAY THAT POGO, OF ALL PEOPLE, IS THE CANDI-DATE, MOLE?
WE SAW HIM BEING FITTED FOR A BUST ON MOUNT RUSHMORE.
3-16
BUT HE'S A GULL AND A DUPE! A FRIENDLY LI'L' DO-GOODER WHO CAN BE PUSHED AROUND BY ANY NINCOMPOOP OR SET OF SAME.
EXACTLY---
--- THAT'S JUST WHERE YOU BOYS COME IN.
And out.

Chapter 10

THE PENETRALIA MENTIS OF A SALAMI

WATCH HIM! ANY GUY WHO FISHES WITHOUT HOOKS IS BOUND TO BE TRUSTWORTHY.
AND, IPSO FACTO, A CANDIDATE ADORED BY THE PEOPLE?
I DUNNO...YOU MEAN HE SENDS THEM POOR BAIT DOWN THERE WITHOUT NOTHIN' TO DEFEND THEIRSELF WITH?
3-19
NO... HE SHOWS HE'S FAIR MINDED, AN ADMIRABLE TRAIT--- HE SETS THE WORMS FREE...NO BAIT!
YOU'RE KIDDIN'! WHAT'S HE CATCH?
WHAT EVER IS IN SEASON...MUMPS, TONSILITIS... ALL LIKE THAT THERE...
D'YOU SUPPOSE IT'S SIGNIFICANT THAT THE MOST SIGNIFICANT PRIMARY, WISCONSIN, ...
THE AUGUST DERLETH
MADISON
3-23

------ COMES SIGNIFICANTLY ON A MOST SIGNIFICANT DAY ? THE DAY AFTER APRIL FOOLS ?
A·D·
SAUK CITY
NO LUCK AGAIN, MR. MIGGLE--- GUESS I'LL HAFTA BUY A FISH--- GOT ANY FRESH ?
HOW FRESH, POGO ?
MIGGLE'S EMPORIUM
MIGGLE'S BOATS & BAITS RENT $1 EACH PER HOUR
3-20
GOT ONE HERE WHAT JUST COME IN FROM A MAIL ORDER HOUSE.
HOW'S THAT?
THAT? THAT'S A SALAMI!
BUT IT'S FRESH! SO FRESH IT TALKS BACK TO YOU--- TRY A PIECE.
OORG--- I SEE WHAT YOU MEAN.
WHY AIN'T IT AGAINST THE LAW TO SEND WEAPONS THRU THE MAIL?

SAY CHEESE, POGO.
CHEESE!
YESSIR! COMIN' RIGHT UP... TWO POUNDS, @ $1.25 PER... THAT'LL BE $2.96, POGO.
SPECIAL! UP-TO-DATE BOLOGNA
MAKE OFFER
QUICK! STOCK UP ON 6¢ STAMPS
NOW
3-21

YESSUH! LET A OL' BUDDY HOL' THIS YERE FOR MY LI'L' OL' BUDDY RIGHT CHERE --- YOU GITTIN' MY GOOD SIDE, OL' BUDDY?
WHICH SIDE'S THAT?

WHO'S INSIDE?
YOUR FRIENDLY NEIGHBORHOOD SALAMI.

Chapter 11

HIS EYE HAS NO PEER

OL' PUP DOG ATE MOST OF THE LEMON SNAPS...GAME'S OVER!
OW! SOME CULPRIT SNUCK A REAL WOODEN CHECKER INTO THE GAME!
I WAS THINKIN', SON, THAT I'D GO INTO A NEW LINE...WHERE IS WE AT RIGHT CHERE NOW?
THIS OVER HERE IS A COMICAL STRIP.
3-26
IN THIS LINE WE LARFS AT BAD JOKES, MAKE FACES; CHASE EACH OTHER WITH GUNS... AN' WE WINK AN' GIGGLE.
SOUND LIKE HOME.
BUT MY EYES! LOOKA THESE YERE FIGGERS. 186 BILLION PLUS 186 BILLION EQUALS 186 BILLION.. RIGHT?
AIN'T NO 186 HERE.... JES' NOTHIN' BUT NAUGHTS.
Y'SEE? I GOT EXTRA DOUBLE VISION...I GO ADDIN' UP ALL THEM ZEE-ROES.

HEY, OL' SON! I HEARS YOU'S THINKIN' OF JOININ' UP WITH US!
YEP... GOT A LI'L' OL' TROUBLE WITH MY LI'L' OL' VISION.
3-27
SO GOTTA GO INTO A NEW LINE... CAN'T SEE MY OLD WORK FOR SHUCKS... MIGHT JUS' A-SWELL BE IN A LI'L' OL' COMICAL STRIP.
BUT IS THAT NEW?
SEE YERE, BOYS... OL' BUDDY POGO SAY HE BE DOUBLE DAGNABBED IF THEY'S 186 BILLION ZEE-ROES YERE.
JES' A SEC', 1·2·3·4~
THIS MAY TAKE A MOMENT OR TWO... WHAT COMES AFTER 127?
HE SHOULD OF STUDIED SPEED READIN'.
WHAT I NEED IS NEW GLASSES, OL' BUDDY.
YESSIR! I'LL SET 'EM RIGHT UP.... YOU'LL HAVE THE USUAL, YOUNG MAN?
TWO CENTS PLAIN.
3-28
AUNT GRANNY'S
DAY OLD ICE 25¢ PER GALLON
PSST... IS HE GOT ANY MONEY?
HE KEEP TALKIN' ABOUT 186 BILLION

SO... GLASSES, EH?
I MEAN I NEED A GOOD EYE DOCTOR.
YESSIR, I'LL BE RIGHT WITH YOU, SIR!... HELP YOU'SELF TO AN ANESTHETIC THERE, SIR.
AUNT GRANNY'S ITTER BRITTLE ROOT
NOW THEN... HERE'S THE CHART.
WHERE, DOC, OL' BUDDY?
THEG RATE FUL SOC IE TY
MIXED FISH AND WIENERS XXX TAKE HOME A SET
3-29
HERE, SIR -- NOW, I UNDERSTAND YOUR VISION IS A LITTLE MITE IMPAIRED.
NO, MY VISION REMAINS: HOW BEAUTIFUL FOR SPACE OR SKIES AND AMPLE WANES OF GRAVES... OH, PIERCEFUL MOUNT OF MAJESTY ABOVE THE FRUITIN' PLAINS... WE WILL DEFEND PEACE AT HOME AND HONOR A-BROAD.
NOT THAT VISION! WHO'S THIS WE GONNA HONOR?
Y'BETTER SET DOWN.

CAIN'T READ A SPECK OF THAT'N, BUDDY.
NOTHIN', HEY?
IDIDN OTEXP ECTTO BEELE CTED PRES IDE NT TO
4-5
HOW 'BOUT THIS'N?
NOSSUH, JES' CAIN'T SEE THAT STUFF.
PRESID EOVERT HEDISS OLUTION OFHERM AJEST Y'SEM PIR E
EVEN IF I COULD READ 'EM, I COULDN'T PRO-NOUNCE 'EM.
WULL, COULD YOU JES' GIMME MAYBE THE GIST OF 'EM?
YOU CALL THAT HIGH CLASS SEEIN'?

Chapter 12

YOU CAN TELEPHONE POLL BUT IT WON'T TOLL BACK

I'LL SHOW YOU·· THE FIRST POLL WE MAKE WILL BE THE TELEPHONE POLL.
4-4
WATCH NOW-- I PUTS IN THE DIME.
OUR SAVINGS!
HELLO?-- IS THIS THE OCCUPANT? I'M MAKIN' A TELEPHONE POLL-- COULD YOU TELL ME TO WHOM YOU ARE LISTENING ON YOUR TELEPHONE AT THIS VERY MOMENT?
SHE HUNG UP SO LOUD SHE KNOCKS ME OFF MY PERCH.
GIT YOUR DIME BACK!
KICK THE MACHINE... AT LEAST GIT SOME GUM!
BEMILDRED, OUR COLLEAGUE, HAS GONE OFF TO POLL MIZ BEAVER--- WE'LL ASK 'BOUT A HUNDERD VOTERS AN' PRO-RATE THE INCUMBENT ON THE SUM OF THE RESIDUE..
TO BE SURE.
4-10
WHAT'S YER OPINION ON THE CHANCES OF THE CANDIDATES? ANSWER HONEST, IF YER HALF-A-MAN...
COR! LUMPIN' POLLSTERS!
HUH? WHAT SYE, MYTE?

I'LL SHOW YER 'OO'S ARF-A-MAN, MYTIE... I SYES A RUM POSITIVE PER'APS!
'EY? WOZZAT? 'ELLO?
WHAT YOU GOT SO FAR?
A TREND.... "Maybe": 1/2 OF 1%..... "Can't hear question": 1%
AND, "Fought back": 1%

CAN YOU READ THIS CHART, SIR?
GO GO, G.O. P.!
SOME CHART! LET'S SAY I CAN READ IT, BUT NEVER COULD SEE IT.
GET WHAT YOU WANT! USE OUR POLL SERVICE
4-11

WELL, HOW 'BOUT THIS'N?
RUNSOF TLYAN DCAR RYAB IGST ICK
THAT'N? "A sampling of three per cent of Population shows ONE % don't know; ONE % don't care and ONE half % says 'maybe'." RIGHT?
OUR POLL EGG-ZACK! THE EYE OF A HAWRK!

SO YOU TADS IS TAKIN' A POLL? OL' BUDDY, I SHO' LIKE POLLS.
YESSIR--- WE WANNA KNOW SHOULD WE PRESS FORWARD?
PRESS ASIDE?
OR PRESS BACK?
1. WE CAN PRESS BACK... 2. PRESS ASIDE AND FINALLY, 3. PRESS FORWARD OR AT ANY RATE WE SHOULD PRESS THAT BRIDGE WHEN WE COME TO IT.
4.12
BUT AT BOTTOM, OUR PEOPLE WILL NEVER. WHETHER IN ADVANCE OR RETREAT, BE DETERRED.
MY VISION IS TO FIGHT THE CREDIBLE DREAM.
WHY'S HE GONNA FIGHT IT?
THERE'S A VISIBILITY GAP THERE.
WE GOT MORE ANSWERS THAN WE GOT QUESTIONS.
NOTES ON VISIONS
NEXT POLLIN' QUESTION--- DO YOU COME FROM A BIG TOWN?
Y'MEAN BIGWISE IN A ACRE-WISE WAY OR FOLKSWISE?
VOTERWISE
WELL, ACTUAL, THEY'S JES' ME AN' MY LI'L' OL' BUDDY..
4.15

HE'S A HOSS.
SO YOU'RE THE ONLY VOTER..
AN' YOUR OPINION MAKES UP 100% OF THEM VOTIN' AN' BREATHIN'.
I B'LEEVE YOU BOYS GOT A FIRM HOLD ON THE GENERAL SITUATION.
WHAT US POLLSTERS WANT TO KNOW IS WHAT'S YOUR OPINION?
ON WHAT?
4-16
WELL, LET'S SEE..
ASK HIM DID HE HAVE ANY GOOD OPINIONS LATELY?
I HEARD THAT.. NO, Y'ALL KNOW OLD OPINIONS ARE LIKE OLD WINE... THE CLOSER TO THE BONE THE SWEETER THE YEAR.
HAD A MIGHTY GOOD OPINION IN 1948 DOWN BY LI'L OL' AUSTIN WAY... A GOOD YEAR FOR IT... ....BUT LATELY? PFAUGH!
HOW YOU SPELL THAT PAFAWG?

MY POLLSTER ASSOCIATES HERE SAID, IN VIEW OF YOUR IMPAIRED VISIONS...
--YOU GOT A VISIBILITY GAP.
INCREDIBLE
4-17
THAT BRINGS UP THE OTHER THING... DO YOU ALSO GOT AN INCREDITABILITY GAP?
HATE TO TELL YOU WHAT I THOUGHT YOU SAID --- Y'KNOW, IN COMPARISON TO MY HEARIN'...
... MY VISIBILITY IS JUS' ABOUT 100 PROOF -- ABOUT LIKE A 30/30.
WHAT ANSWER DO YOU GIT?
WELL, WHERE ARE WE?
ABOUT HALF WAY THRU THE BOOK.
COMIN' OR GOIN'?

Chapter 13

BOLSTER YOUR POLLSTER, BUSTER

I HEAR YOU BATS IS TAKIN' A POLL...
YEP... ANY ANSWER YOU WANTS, WE'LL GET A QUESTION FOR IT.
AIM TO PLEASE, HUH?
YESSIR! AS OF THE RACE TODAY, WHO DO YOU LIKE?
4-11A
MMM...
....HOW ABOUT PLACE AN' SHOW, TWO AN' TWO, ON TURKEY TROTSKY IN THE FOURTH?
HMM... THINK THAT'LL HOLD UP; RIGHT INTO OREGON?
WHAT OTHER KIND OF QUESTIONS DO YOU POLLSTERS POSE?
WE ASK OF THEM IN THE HEADWATERS: IF WE PRESS FORWARD, SHOULD WE THEN PRESS ASIDE... OR PRESS BACK OR PRESS THAT OL' BRIDGE WHEN WE COME TO IT....?
4-12 A

THEN, WITH OUR PEOPLE IN ADVANCE OR RETREAT, WOULD YOU STILL FIGHT THE INCREDIBLE DREAM?
I GET A MEMORY GAP ALONG THERE SOME ERES.
A NEW ANSWER! USUALLY, 100% REPLIES = HUH?
FOR ONE BAT, YOU SURE POLL A LOT OF PEOPLE...
NOT REALLY... THERE'S THREE OF ME!
4-15 A
ONE IS ALL I SEE... ARE YOU WEARIN' TRI-FOCALS?
LOOK YONDER.
MY BROTHERS, BEWITCHED, AN' BOTHERED... I GO BY NAME BEMILDRED, TODAY. THEY'RE INTER-VIEWIN' EACH OTHER.
HOW DO YOU TELL YOUR-SELVES A-PART?
BY OUR PANTS... ACCORDIN' TO WHICH PAIR YOU PUT ON IN THE MORNING, THAT'S WHO YOU ARE THAT DAY.

YOU POLLSTERS GET YOUR RESULTS BY AVERAGING OUT THE ANSWERS OF YES OR NO?
YES AN' NO.
NOW THEN, SIR. YOU AN' ME LIVES WITH HIM, RIGHT?
RIGHT!
RIGHT!
4-16A
RIGHT! WODDYA THINK OF HIM ?
BARELY TOLERABLE, RIGHT?
RIGHT! HOW 'BOUT WITH HIS CLOTHES ON?
RIGHT! SAME WAY.
RIGHT! I AGREES... THAT'S 100% OF THOSE INTERVIEWED THINK HE'S UNSPEAKABLE, RIGHT?
RIGHT--- FINAL PERCENT AVERAGE MIGHT BE A LITTLE HIGHER.
YA GOIN'?
RIGHT! TO REDUCE THE AVERAGE RIGHT?
I WAS JUST TELLING MR. LA FEMME, HERE, THAT POGO IS AN EXCELLENT DARK HORSE...
AN' I WAS JUS' TALKIN' TO THE POLLSTER BATS.
POTATO CRIPS
4-17A
THEY FIGURE IF YOU'RE THE ONLY ONE VOTIN' AN' BREATHIN' HERE, THEN 100% OF THEM NOT POLLED FEEL THE SAME AS YOU.
POTATO

THERE ARE SOME RESIDENT MICE AND A GHASTLY GROUP OF SPIDERS, TO BE FAIR.
OLD ENUF TO VOTE ?
DID YOU EVER SEE A 21 YEAR OLD MOUSE OR ARACHNID ?
GACK! THEN YOU GOT 100% THINKS THE POSSUM IS A EXCELLENT DARK HORSE.
POTATO CRIPS
Y'KNOW WHAT OL' MOLE SAYS? POGO IS A NATURAL DARK-HORSE.
WHAT'S THESE?
4-18
CAMPAIGN BUTTONS FOR OL' POG', NATCH...
GACK!
I'M A GONER... I ATE ONE... THUNK THEY WAS POTATO CHIPS.
BUT.. HEH HEH..
I'M POISONED! HELP!
THEY IS POTATO CHIPS, MY DEAR SIR!

PULL OUT THE PULMOTOR---I'M DEAD!..SWALLOWED A CAMPAIGN BUTTON!
COME BACK!---THAT CAMPAIGN BUTTON WAS EMINENTLY EDIBOBBLE! A POTATO CHIP!
ALL'S I PRINTED ON IT WAS POGO FOR PRES! DARK-HORSE-POWER!
4-19
'CAUSE POGO'S A DARK-HORSE; SEE?
WHAT'S WRONG WITH DARK-HORSE-POWER?
I'M DEAD! I ATE A POGO CAMPAIGN BUTTON!
IT WAS A POTATO CHIP!
4-20
WHY IN THE WORLD IS YOU PRINTIN' CAMPAIGN BUTTONS ON POTATO CHIPS?
WHEN YOU'S THROUGH WITH A CANDIDATE, GLOP! DOWN THE LAUNDRY CHUTE...

MAN! THAT WAS A CLOSE CALL...ONLY MY MEDIWOCKLE KNOW-HOW PULLED ME THROUGH.
HEY, PORKY, I'M PRINTIN' POGO CAMPAIGN BUTTONS ON POTATO CHIPS.. SO YOU CAN EAT 'EM.
POGO
A GREAT IDEA FOR ALL CANDIDATES--- THEY COULD WRITE THEIR SPEECHES ON, SAY, PANCAKES AN' THEN--.

OL' MOLE SAID POGO IS A NATURAL-BORN DARK-HORSE--- SO I MADE THESE BUTTONS FOR HIM--- DARK-HORSE POWER.
BUT, MEBBE FOLKS IS LOOKIN' FOR A MAN ON A WHITE HORSE... WHITE-HORSE-POWER..
YESSUH! COMIN' RIGHT UP!
4-22

WELL! AREN'T YOU JUST A LITTLE CHICKEN?
NOSSUH! PRINCE POMPADOODLE AIN'T NO WAYS, NO HOW, A-FRAID OF NO-BODY.

SO YOU'RE FOR WHITE HORSEPOWER? MEANIN' THE MAN ON THE WHITE HORSE?
YESSUH! AS OPPOSED TO POGO'S DARK HORSE-POWER.
4-23
I MADE BUTTONS FOR POGO SAYIN' "DARK HORSEPOWER," SHOULD I MAKE SOME FOR YOU?
NOSSUH.. I ALREADY GOT ALL MY BUTTONS.
KLUNK!
AWK!
THE SKY'S FALLING!
CHICKEN LITTLE!
FIGGERS
HUH?
I SAID, THE SKY IS FALLIN'.. GOTTA RUSH AN' WARN EVERY MIDDLESEX, VILLAGE AN' FARM.
4-24
YOU'RE THE WHITE HORSEPOWER GUY... THERE'S A OLD UNEMPLOYED WHITE HORSE...
COME ON, BOOST ME UP.. I'LL BE THE MAN ON THE WHITE HORSE.

FORWARD!
PRINCE POMPADOODLE IS RIDIN' THRU THE LAND TO WARN THE PEOPLE TO ARM THEIRSELVES --- THE SKY IS FALLIN'.
TO ARMS! TO ARMS! EVERY MIDDLE-SEX VILLAGE AN' FARM.
BACK-WARDS?
4-25
FORWARD!
THE PRINCE IS FORWARD ENOUGH!
STRANGE HE'D ASSOCIATE HIMSELF WITH THAT END OF THE HORSE.
IT WAS THE ONLY ONE IN SERVICE.

YOU SAID POGO WAS A NATURAL-BORN DARK HORSE SO I MADE UP SOME DARK HORSEPOWER BUTTONS... THAT FELLOW WHAT'S FOR WHITE HORSEPOWER DIN'T WANT ANY.
4-26
THE PRINCE OF POMPADOODLE THERE, THE MAN ON THE WHITE HORSE, I LIKE THE CUT OF HIS JIB.
WHAT'S THE DIFFERMINTS? WHITE HORSEPOWER, DARK HORSEPOWER... IT'S WHO'S RIDIN' THE HORSE THAT COUNTS.
THERE HE IS, THE PRINCE OF POMPADOODLE ON A WHITE HORSE!
HEY, PRINCE, YOU'RE GOIN' BACKWARDS..
NOT ME... THE HORSE IS GOIN BACKWARD! I'M GOIN' FORWARD!
HOW CAN THE HORSE SEE WHERE HE'S GOIN'?
5-3

WITH ME IN THE SADDLE, WHY SHOULD HE?
OOP!
HOPE THE HORSE CAN SWIM.
IF NOT, MEBBE THE PRINCE IS A JUNIOR LIFEGUARD.
MAN! I'D LIKE TO KNOW HOW THEM BATS WORKS THEIR POLLS.
JES' LIKE ALL THE OTHER ONES DO.
HANGAR 14
THE S.S. PARSONS
5-4
HOW'S THAT?
YOU TELL THEM BAT POLLSTERS WHAT ANSWER YOU WANT AND THEY WORKS OUT A FORMULA OF QUESTIONS TO GET IT... PRESTO! INSTANT PLACEBO!
THE IDLEWILD ROCKET
CAPTAIN DAVID

Chapter 14

THE RACE IS TO THE SHIFT

ONE OF MY Wind-ups ★ ON HIS WAY to the Massachusetts PRIMARY RACE... He LOOKS PROMISING!
WHAT DO HE PROMISE?
NO MORE WAR GAMES
WHOLLY GRAIL
4-29

Always PROMISE ☆MORE☆
WON'T GET NOWHERES PROMISIN' 'NO MORE' OF ANYTHIN'
HE OUGHTTA GET ON THAT JAZZY MULE... HE'D MOVE FASTER!
WHO'S THAT HITCHIN' A RIDE?
SOMETIMES IT'S BETTER TO NOT BE ENCUMBERED WITH A MULE.
TWEET

WHOLLY GRAIL
JUST WANT TO GET A SHOT OF THE WHITE KNIGHT HERE -- YOU'LL STAY IN THE RACE, SIR?
4-30

YES!
OH, SO YOU'RE IN THE PICTURE, SIR?

I'M IN TO THE BITTER END.
THE BETTER END IS USUALLY THE START...
I SAID BITTER
CAN'T TELL -- MIGHT BE EITHER, BOTH OR OTHERWISE.... SAY "CHEESE."
CHEESE
HERE he comes BACK... PROBABLY made OUT POORLY.
AT LEAST HE'S ON THE MULE NOW...
WHOLLY GRAIL
LET ME SHOW YOU THE WAY FROM HERE ON
5-1
TOO BAD! ☆ I KNEW IT!
MORNING RACE RESULTS SHOWS HE DID GOOD...
SEE? I KNEW it! a COMER!!! ☆
WHICH?!

HOW DID YOU LIKE THE MASSACHUSETTS RACE?
WELL, LET'S JUS SAY, OUR POLLS WERE PROVEN OUT 100%.
ON THE NOSE.
5-2
GOLLY... NOT EVEN THE BEST OTHER POLLS COME OUT A HUNDERD PER.
IT MAKES A MAN PROUD TO KNOW ANY FOLKS IN THIS SWAMP KIN BE 100% RIGHT.
I'M AFRAID YOU MISUNDERSTOOD, SIR--- WE DIN'T MEAN 100% RIGHT.
ORG..... YOU MEANT 100% THE OTHER WAY?
SOMETHIN' LIKE THAT.
?
YOU SAID IT.

Chapter 15

EAT CROW À LA MOOD

HAD I CHOSEN TO RUN IN INDIANA I WOULD OF WON IN A WALK.
THE NOBLE UNDERDOG!
5-7
RIGHT! AT THE BATTLE OF LITTLE BIG HORN WHO WAS THE FIRST INDIAN ASHORE? THE NOBLE DOG!
INDIANA! WHAT DID THAT NOBLEST HOOSIER, WASHINGTON, SAY TO THE NOBLE DOG AS THEY CROSSED THE WABASH?
MAN! WHAT?
HE SAYS, SET DOWN, HE SAYS, YOU'RE ROCKIN' THE BOAT!
BRAVO!
WHO INVITED ALL THESE DANG CROWS TO OUR PICNIC?
THIS NEWSPAPER YOU WRAPPED THE EGG FOO YOUNG IN SAYS WORLD MONEY IS USUAL BASED ON PRECIOUS METALS...
5-9
WE OUGHT TO BASE MONEY ON SOMETHIN' WE COULD EAT!

SUCH AS? S'IL VOUS PLAIT, N'EST-CE PAS?
SUCH AS CROW... IN THIS PRESIDENTAL YEAR.
MAN, I'D GIVE A PERTY TO KNOW HOW THESE CROWS GOT WIND OF OUR PICNIC!
THE BREEZES FROM THE CHURCHY FIRE IS BLOW THE STENCH OF THE PERLOO PERHAP?
MISS STEPHANIE
5-10
PERHAPPLES... BUT WHENCE DID THEY ALL COME FROM?
EGGS... IS A VERY BIG YEAR FOR LAY THE EGG.
TWO GUN
S.S. STELLA

THERE HE GO··· OL' BEAUREGARD, THE UNDERDOG CANDIDATE!
QUALIFICATIONWISE, WHAT'S HIS ASSETS? ASSETWISE SPEAKING?
5-17
WELL, HE GOT A HEART··· THE NOBLE HEART OF A TRUE DOG··· MAN'S BEST FRIEND.
HOW IS HE BRAINWISE?
BRAINWISE!? WELL! HE GOT A BRAIN ON HIM. THINKINGWISE HE GOT A REAL MIND ON HIM. MINDWISE SPEAKING, OF COURSE···
BUT WHAT KINDA BRAIN YOU GOT IN MIND, CASUALLY-SPEAKINGWISE? YOU MEAN THOUGHTWISE··· OR MEBBE MEMORYWISE··· OR KEENWISE?
HOW 'BOUT WISEWISE?
WHICH-WISE?

Chapter 16

THE PONDERANCE OF PONDER

KEEP AN EYE ON POGO, THE DARK HORSE, THE CANDIDATE OF DARK HORSE-POWER...
CONSIDER IT DONE.
POGO'S THE KEY TO CONTROL OF THE ELECTION; DARK HORSEPOWER-- I'D LIKE TO TIE HIM UP.
5-11
I THOUGHT YOU LIKED THE OTHER GUY.
I DO.
WHEN I SAY "TIED UP" I MEAN IN THE OLD FASHIONED SENSE... TIED UP DOWN THE CELLAR... WITH A HEMP COLLAR-- DIFFICULT TO RUN THAT WAY.
SO I'D SUPPOSE.
WHAT ARE YOU ALL DRESSED UP FOR, MOLE?
I'M DISGUISED AS A DOGCATCHER.
5-20
YOU'RE GOING TO HAVE A MESS OF HYSTERICAL DOGS ON YOUR HANDS.
I'M NOT AFTER DOGS...

I'M AFTER POGO, THE CANDIDATE.
HOW'RE YOU, AS DOG-CATCHER, GONNA JUSTIFY PUTTIN' THE NAB ON A POSSUM?
BAD EYESIGHT
MOLE'S TAKEN LEAVE OF HIS SO-CALLED SENSES...
Years ago.
5-21
HE'S SLIPPED ANOTHER COG... HE'S KIDNAPPING THE CANDIDATE, POGO.
A great idea --- He'll hold him 'til Election Day --- Then ransom him off.
IT'LL COST A FORTUNE... HE'LL HAFTA FEED HIM.
Not if I know old Mole.

THE PERFECT CANDIDATE... TRUSTING, DEPENDABLE, A PERFECT GENTLEMAN AND A PERFECT DUPE.
IF I CAN CAPTURE HIM...I CAN CONTROL HIM...AND A NATION! AND TOMORROW THE UNIVERSE.
MY ASSOCIATES THINK I DREAM TOO MUCH...THAT MY VISION, MY IDEAL IS IMPOSSIBLE... THEY CALL ME MAD!
ME! MAD?! HEH HEH HEH!
HE'LL NEVER KNOW WHO I AM..
AND HE'LL NEVER EVEN SEE ME
OR KNOW WHAT HIT HIM...

MORNIN', MOLE... NICE DAY..
OL' CHARLIE
DIDN'T MEAN TO FALL INTO YOUR BOAT, POGO.... I UNDERSTAND YOU, LIKE EVERYBODY, IS RUNNIN' FOR PRESIDENT... AND YOU'LL WIN!
ME? I'M A BONA FIDE NON-CANDIDATE.
5-24
BUT, THE WAY I GET IT, YOU'RE A BONA FIDE SHOO-IN NON-CANDIDATE.

Gentlemen!
It's ☞ ON To Oregon! We'll vote Early AND OFTEN!
EARLY AND OFTEN? WE CAN'T!
5-25
Why, PRAY ☜ ☞ TELL, ---------- NOT?!
OUTSIDERS CAN'T VOTE.
THEY CAN RUN CAN'T THEY?
WE'LL TAKE ANOTHER BOAT, P.T. --- IT'S EASIER'N TURNIN' THAT ONE OVER.

Chapter 17

THE PRIMARY TARGET PRIMED

YEAH, WE'RE HAVIN' A PRIMARY ELECTION... WODDYA THINK WE'RE DOIN'?
OH, IS THIS OREGON, THEN?
OREGON? NOSSUH, THIS HERE'S NORTH FLORIDA.
5-28
THINK OREGON'S THE ONLY ONE CASTIN' A BALLOT TODAY?
CHARLIE, GIT 'ROUN' ON THE BUSH SIDE YONDER AND VOTE FROM THERE.
LET'S POLL ON OUT, P.T.
I BEEN TO THE PRIMARY...
MY SAKES! THAT'S FAST... HOW DID YOU GO?
MUST OF FLEW!
WENT BY SKIFF... ROWED AND POLED ALL THE WAY.
GRONK!
GOZZLE!
5-29

O JOY! HALLOO! HALLAY!
SMACK! SMACK!
WE'RE FAMOUS! A OKEFENOKEE FIRST! ALLAWAY ACROSS THE CONTINENT BY OAR! OREGON!
NOT OREGON... FLORIDA! OVER YONDER, DOWN-TOWN A BIT.
COULDENT YOU OF TOLE ME THAT AFORE I KISSED HIM?
LOOK, POGO, A COUNTY WHAT AIN'T GOT A CANDIDATE JUS' AIN'T WITH IT...
UM?
RIGHT.
5-30
THE BATS INTERVIEWED A SAMPLE OF FAIR MINDED, SMART CITIZENS HERE AN' IT SHOWS THE SWAMP IS 100% FOR YOU.
WHOM WAS THE SAMPLE?
ME AN' HIM.
YOU'LL WIN IN A WALK.
WON'T BE HURRYIN', THAT'S SURE--- SO YOU WANT A NON-CANDIDATE TO RUN A NON-RACE TO WIN A NON-OFFICE?
YOU'LL DO IT?
HOO BOY!
WHAT A SENSE OF SACKERFICE!

HEY, PORKY! POGO SAYS HE'LL RUN!
OH, FRABJOUS DAY!
FER WHERE?
5-31
HOW'D YOU GET TO THIS SPOT? WAS YOU DRUGGED?
ALL THE WAY!
WE SHOULD OF ENDED THIS STRIP BACK THERE ... THE SNAPPER'S IN THE MIDDLE.
WE'LL CHANGE THE NAME TO OPOG.
?
IT'S POGO TURNED INSIDE-OUT.
SO POGO WILL RUN! ... THE COUNTRY WILL BE SAVED! WHAT IS SO RARE AS A DAY IN OCTOBER?
NOVEMBER THE SIXST.
6-1
TWO CANDIDATES BACK FROM OREGON!
ON THEIR WAY TO CALIFORNIA!

WONDER IF THEY STILL SEES EYE-TO-EYE?
AND TOOTH-TO-TOOTH?

I TOLE CHURCHY AN' OWL THEY WANTED A NON-CANDIDATE TO RUN A NON-RACE FOR A NON-OFFICE... THEY FIGGERED IT MEANT I'D RUN..
WHY DIN'T YOU GIVE 'EM A FLAT NO?
TO THEM, THAT WOULD OF BEEN A LI'L AMBIGUOUS...
6-3

C'MON, POGO! WE'RE GONNA GIVE YOU A TORCH-LIGHT PARADE.

ON TO CALIFORNIA!
SEE!? HE'S THEIR HERO!
WHAT THEY GONNA DO? SET FIRE TO HIM?

Chapter 18

A WALK ON THE WEIRD SIZE

MR. CANDIDATE, EVER NOTICE, IN THIS SWAMP...
MY OLD HOME TOWN... SWAMP OF MY SALAD DAYS...
6-5
FOLKS IS ALL-AWAYS WALKIN' SOMEPLACE.. REAL FAST..
AN' GITTIN' NOWHERES.
WHERE'S TO GO?
BUT.. YOU COULD SAY THE SAME FOR A LOT WHAT'S RUNNIN', TOO.
NO FAIR! YOU'RE RUNNIN'!
G-ROWF!
6-6
MY WORD!
I MERELY, AM INDULGIN' IN A DOGLY TROT... USING ALL FOUR HANDS.

FOUR HANDS? HEY!
SWISH!
ALBERT! I WISH YOU'D STOP BLUNDERING INTO MY TRAPS!
GEE.... SORRY, MOLE.
THAT ALBERT! ALMOST SPOILED MY TRAP FOR POGO.
6-7
AHA! A--
--HA!
?
HA! HEE-HEE! GOT HIM!

WHAT YOU GOT THERE, MOLE?
HEE HEE! THE CANDIDATE I WAS AFTER.
6-8
YOU MEAN POGO?
YEH... SHHHH... EVEN THE TREES GOT EARS.
HEAR THAT? WHAT'D I TELL YOU?
YOU INSIST YOU'VE GOT POGO IN THAT SACK?
YES! AND LOWER YOUR VOICE.
6-10
REALLY? POGO?
YES.. QUIET! HE'S VERY CLEVER.

YOU'RE DANGBANG RIGHT, MOLE... VERY CLEVER!
HE'S MET HIS MATCH THIS TIME.

HEE-HEE.... THEY'RE RUNNING OFF ANOTHER PRIMARY IN ILLINOIS TODAY... TO HELP DETERMINE THE CANDIDATE... HEE HEE! AND ALL THE TIME I'VE GOT THE REAL CANDIDATE, POGO!
6-11

IN THE BAG! HEE-HEE! THEY'RE WASTING THEIR TIME!
WELL... THEY AIN'T ALONE.

ARE YOU THE ONLY AND ORIGINAL POGO?
NO... I'M THE POGO PRESENT AN' BREATHIN'... THE ORIGINAL WENT TO HIS REWARD DIRECTLY AFTER THE BATTLE OF BULL RUN.
MISS BERNICE
6-12
MOLE SAY HE GOT POGO, THE CANDIDATE, IN THE BAG UP YONDER IN THE SHACK.
WELL, I'M TRYIN' TO BE POGO, THE NON-CANDIDATE.
MOLE'S A LITTLE TOUCH CORN-FUSED.
MEBBE HE GOT NON-POGO, THE CANDIDATE.
BERNICE ELEANOR
DALLAS

HEE--HEE...
SO YOU THINK YOU GOT POGO IN THAT SACK, MOLE, RIGHT?
6-13
DID YOU FALL OVERBOARD WHEN YOU WERE GOIN' AFTER POGO, BY ANY CHANCE, OL' SON?
HOW'D YOU GUESS?

TAKE A LOOK, MY OPIC FRIEND.
PLOP!
MY WORD...HE LOOKS SORTA PEAKIED.... ...GOT A BAD COUGH TOO.
ROWF!
MUMP! MUMP! MUMP! MUMP!
I GOT IT RIGHT HERE! MY MAIDEN SPEECH FOR A PRIMARY ELECTION.
BULLY FOR YOU...LET A COUPLE EXPERTS GIVE IT A EAR.
AHEM, LADIES AN' GENTLEMEN.. AHEM! AHEM-- HUM-- AHEM-- AHEM!
GREAT START.
6-14

I RISE TO GIVE YOU A MAN WHO FEARS NAUGHT, A MAN WHO IS LOVED BY ALL, A MAN WHO IS THE BORN LEADER OF ALL --
WHO'S THAT? IF THIS GUY'S THAT GOOD, TAKE YOUR HAT OFF-.
WOULDN'T THAT BE A BIT IMMODEST? ME TO TAKE MY HAT OFF IN HONOR OF ME?
OH, THE THINGS I COULD SAY ABOUT THIS MAN.
AS UNDERDOG CANDIDATE, THE NOBLE DOG STANDS WITH HAND OUTSTRETCHED, READY TO GIVE OR RECEIVE --
BROTHER!
6-15
MAN'S BEST FRIEND IS READY TO HELP ALL, READY TO AGAIN BE NOBLE AT THE RAMPARTS.
THANK YOU FOR YOUR HEARTFELT, ADORING GRATITUDE AND FOR MY WELL-DESERVED APPLAUSE.
WHEE! HOO BOY! HOORAY FOR THE UNDERDOG!
THING I LIKE ABOUT HIM IS HIS SINCERITY-

Chapter 19

A WORD TO THE FORE IS "HELP!"

FORE! OOF!
HEAR THAT? IT DOES SOUND LIKE THE MATING CRY OF THE WILD NIBLICK.
6-18
FORE!
ROWRF!
FORE! DAGRABBIT!
LOOKY THERE! IT LAID A EGG!
SO THAT'S A NIBLICK?
IT'S WILD ENOUGH!
AARG
ROWR
YOWF
THAT LOOKS LIKE OL' MOLE... NOT NO WILD NIBLICK.
SO IT IS... WHAT WAS WE TALKIN' ABOUT?
FLASHIN' BASH-BAGGLED GOLF BALL!
6-19
MOST BROKE-UP CONVERSATION WE EVER HAD!
CAN'T REMEMBER WHAT IT WAS BUT I'LL NEVER FORGET IT...

LAND! THE OL' FEATHERS IN THAT NEST.
IS POGO GOT ANYTHING IN HIS ICE BOX, ALBERT?
YOU DON'T THINK I'D LOOK, DO YOU?
POGO
6-20

LAND!

POGO
WHAT'S IN IT?
COLD MUSH AN' SLAW.
SNOW? IN JUNE?

IT'S THE DREAD BLUE NORTHER!
SNOW! A JUNE BLIZZARD!
A CHINOOK!
6-21

THEM FEATHERS!
GIT INDOORS.

START A FIRE!
ONLIEST PAPER IS THE CALENDAR.
JUNE 21
I'M FREEZIN'
JUST IN TIME--I'LL PAD THE DOOR.
DEC. 1
YEH--KEEP THEM WINDS OUT-- BRRR
WOOD!
JUNE 21
MEN, HERE WE IS...BRRR... TRAPPED IN A BLIZZARD-- BUT POOR POGO! HE'S OUT THERE IN THIS THING.
POOR DEAR POGO.
6-22
ONE OF US GOTTA GIT A GOOD MEAL IN HIM AN' GO OUT AN' GIT GOOD OL' POGO--- MM ONLIEST THING BESIDES COLD MUSH AN' SLAW IS CANNED GOODS--WHERE'S A OPENER?
GOOD OL' POGO.
PORK WINGS
PINE CONES
CAT BAIT
GOOD OL' POGO.
I JUS' RECALLS, GOOD OL' POGO ALLUS CARRIES HIS OPENER ON HIM-- A SAFETY MEASURE.
HOW SNEAKY!
WELL, HE'S ON HIS OWN.
WHAT A PAL!
DEC. 1

Chapter 20

A LONG, SHOT WINTER

WHEN YOU KICKED MY NOSE UP ACCIDENTALLY, IT STUCK!
6-25
I TAKE BACK WHAT I SAID... YOU DON'T LOOK LIKE POGO'S GRAN'PA... THAT'S THE TRUTH.
THANK YOU, SAM, I SORT OF RESENTED THAT... GLAD YOU SEE THE TRUTH...
YUP... I DO... YOU LOOK MORE LIKE POGO AT THE AGE OF 102.
HEH... IF I CAN'T CAPTURE POGO... I'LL DISGUISE MYSELF AS POGO... I'LL BE THE CANDIDATE!
WITH THAT NEW UPTURNED SCHNOZ OF YOURS YOU LOOK LIKE A MORE OR LESS MEMBER OF HIS FAMILY...A REMITTANCE MAN.
6-26

WITH THE FUR HAT AN' THE PAJAMA JACKET··· NOW I DON'T LOOK LIKE HIS GRAN'PA, DO I?

LEMME GET A CLEAR BEAD ON YOU, MOLE··· NO, YOU'RE RIGHT··· YOU DON'T LOOK LIKE HIS GRAN'PA···
YOU LOOK LIKE HIS GRAN'MOMMA.

NOBODY WILL RECOGNIZE ME HEE HEH-HA
H'LO MOLE

THERE, I OPENED THE CANS WITH THE AXE···WE WON'T STARVE FOR LACK OF A CAN-OPENER.
GOOD JOB!
DEC
1
I THINK I'LL GO AFTER POGO IN THIS BLIZZARD ···CAN'T BEAR THE THOUGHT OF HIM OUT THERE ALONE.
6-27

HAT! COAT! RUBBERS! SNOW GOGGLES! ALPENSTOCK!
BRANDY CASK!
I SAID I THINK I'LL GO...
POGO
BRRR CLOSE THE DOOR.
HERE I IS OUT IN A HOWLIN' BLIZZARD ON A ERRAND OF MERCY LIKE A SAM BERNARD.
6-28
DO I SEE WHAT I SEE OR IS THE HOTTEST JUNE 28 SINCE 18-NAUGHTY-9 STRANGLED MY EYE-BONES?
YOU SEES WHAT YOU SEES.
WHAT WAS IT?
WHATEVER IT WAS, IT WAS WORTH FOR-GETTIN'.
POGO! IT'S YOU! DIMLY SEEN THRU THIS BLIZZARD.
HE THINKS I'M POGO! A STROKE OF LUCK...BUT I DON'T KNOW WHICH KIND.

COME BACK HERE, POGO! THIS BLIZZARD DISTORTS YOUR IMAGE... I CAN HAR'LY SEE YOU IN THE FREEZIN' COLD!
THIS GUY IS A 100 PROOF NUT!
CHASIN' ME... ALL DRESSED LIKE THAT... ON THE HOTTEST DAY SINCE THE CHICAGO FIRE.
7-1
I'M A GONER... THE HEAT GOT ME.
POGO! POGO! YOU COLLAPSED... THE SUB-ZERO COLD IS GOT YOU!
YOU'LL FREEZE... DON'T GO TO SLEEP, IT'S FATAL... CURL UP IN THE BLANKET... DRINK THE SAM BERNARD BRANDY!
LEMME IN... I GOT HIM!
YOU FOUND POGO!
7-2
SAVED FROM THE BLIZZARD ALIVE!
THANKS TO THE SAM BERNARD BRANDY...
GOOD OL' POG'
THRUSH TONGUE

YEH, IF I DIN'T OF DRUNK THAT, I'D OF NEVER MADE IT BACK.
OH, I PERSON'LY IS OVER-JOYED.
DEC. 1
NOW WE CAN FRISK GOOD OL' POG' FOR HIS GOOD OL' CAN OPENER...
FIG STEW
LUMP STEW
SAUEK KKU
LIFT HIM UP INTO THE BED...
MAN! HE'S KIND OF HEAVY AND SWOLE UP... NOT LIKE POGO ATALL! HE LOOK FUNNY WITH SNOW GOGGLES.
DEC 1
MEBBE POOR OL' POG SWOLE UP FROM BEIN' FROZE IN THE SNOW.
7-3
I DON'T BEE-LIEVE THE SWOLES SET IN 'TIL YOU STARTS TO DEE-COMPOSE...
DEC
GUNK!

Chapter 21

HOT WATER IS SOLUBLE IN THE SOLUTION

OKAY, NOW, POGO...I PUT ICE IN YOUR TOO-HOT BATH.
AN' LEMON AN' SUGAR..
..IN CASE YOU GOES UNDER.
IN WHICH CASE YOU GOT A LIFEGUARD STANDIN' BY.
7-9
GET HIM! HE AIN'T COMIN' BACK UP!
I'LL GRAB HIM BY THE...
...HAIR!?
YOU SCALPED HIM!
MY EVER-LOVIN' BLUE EYES! I DID SCALP THE BOY!....ALBEIT UNWITTINGLY...
POGO'S KNOCKED OFF WITH ALL THE HOT AN' COLD BATHS.
UNLESS YOU HANGS THAT SCALP ON THE TEPEE, YOU GOTTA GIT IT BACK ON HIM.
7-10

HOW'LL I MAKE IT STICK?
HERE... THE VERY THING.
ARE YOU NUTS? YOU WANNA NAIL IT ON?
YEAH... YOU MUST BE A IMBECILE... THIS IS A RUSTY NAIL.... YOU WANT HIM TO CATCH THE LOCKJAW?
HEY! WHEN IS THEM POLITIWOCKLE CONVENTIONS? AUGUST, AIN'T THEY?
YEP... PUT POOR OL' POGO OVER ON THE BED, OWL.
DEC. 1
7-11
'CORDIN' TO THIS CALENDAR, THE CONVENTIONS AND THE ELECTIONS IS OVER.
I'LL BE DADNURBED! NO WONDER WE HAD SNOW...
Y'KNOW HE LOOK KINDA GOOD WITH PLAIN GLUE.

IMAGINE! WE MUST OF BEEN SNOWED-IN FOR MONTHS.
IF YOU SPECKS POGO'S HAIR TO GROW BACK YOU GOTTA JAZZ IT UP SOME.
HOW 'BOUT I MIXES FERTILIZER WITH THE GLUE?
DEC. 1
GRO
7-12

THERE IT IS! PLAIN AS PLAIN! DECEMBER! THE ELECTIONS IS OVER...
WHOOSH! THAT'S AWFUL LOUD FERTILIZER... YOU'D DO HIM A FAVOR TO SET HIS HEAD OUTSIDE TO AIR OFF.
I'LL WRAP IT UP IN A BANDAGE.
DEC 1

IF ELECTION DAY IS COME AN' GONE, WHO'S PRESIDENT?
SHH... THE PATIENT IS RESTIN' COMFY.
WONDER IF HE'S DONE?
DEC. 1
7-15
GRONK!
HE'S BERSERK!

GOOCH!
GWEEP!
MAN! ALL THAT CARRYIN' ON AFTER ALL WE DID FOR HIM.
LIKE WHAT?
WE PUT A CURE ON HIS HEAD... HOT LEMONADE WITH GLUE AN' A BIG CLOD OF FERTILIZER...
WHAT'S THE CURE FOR THE CURE?
THE FERTILIZER WAS PUT ON HIS HEAD TO GROW HIS HAIR BACK.
YOU GOTTA SOAK IT OFF IN HOT LEMONADE AGAIN... IT'S DRIVIN' HIM NUTS!
7-16
ALL RIGHT! EASY IN! LET IT SOAK!
DEC
1
HE MUST BE MAD AT US...
YEH... HE'S NOT SPEAKIN' TO US.

STAND BACK!
KRONKIT!
7-17
HE FELL RIGHT ON HIS POOR BANDAGED SCHNOZ...
GOONCH!
HE TOOK THE GOOK OFF HIS HEAD! HIS NOSE IS BENT AWRY...
POOR POGO! GEE! YOU BENT YOUR NOSE DOWN OUTTA SHAPE... YOU GOT A CASE OF THE UGLIES... YOU LOOK JES' LIKE... SQUINNY OLD MOL...
ORG! LIKE, UGH, MOLE! LIKE OL' UGLE MOLE.
HERE, I'LL HOLD POGO... YOU GUYS PUSH HIS NOSE BACK UP INTO SHAPE.
NO! NO!
YOU DON'T WANT TO GO AROUND LOOKIN' LIKE OL' MOLE, DO YA, POG'?
7-18
I FIGGER WE TAKES THE SPANNER AN' UNSCREWS HIS SCHNOZ AROUND TO THE NORTH..
EMINENT!

THEN YOU WON'T RESEMBLE THAT UGLY MOLE.. HEY, C'MERE!
POODAD!
GLOMMIS?

HE RUSHIN' OUT INTO THE BLIZZARD.
POOR POGO! HE'LL FREEZE!
LEAVE HIM! AFTER ALL WE DID! LET HIM BE A INGRATE.

RUN RUN RUN.. IF I EVER HEAR THE NAME POGO AGAIN.. RUN RUN RUN RUN.. RUN RUN..
7-19

RUN RUN -- IF I DO--RUN RUN RUN... I'LL COMMIT...

HEY, OL' MOLE!
--MURDER!

'SMATTER, IS HE MAD?
AT WHAT?
RUN RUN

Chapter 22

NO DEPOSITS, NO RETURNS?

COME ON IN HERE, SON... I WANNA SHOW YOU SOMETHIN' WE FOUND DURIN' THE LATE BLIZZARD.
DEC 1
7-22
SEE THERE? DECEMBER, THE ONE... THE ELECTION'S OVER!
DEC. 1
WHAT?
IF THAT'S SO... WHO WON?
NOT ME ANYWAYS.
DEC 1
CONGRATULATIONS.
BEATS ME HOW THE ELECTIONS SKUN PAST WITHOUT ANYBODY NOTICIN'.
THAT CALENDAR, DECEMBER FIRST, IS IN BLACK AN' WHITE... IT DON'T LIE.
7-23
THERE'S ANOTHER GUY WHAT DIN'T NOTICE.
AND I SAY UNTO YOU, I GIVE YOU A MAN WHO IS SKILLED, WHO KNOWS WHAT TIME IT IS...

MAYBE WE SHOULD ALERT HIM THAT HE'S WASTIN' HIS TIME.
UM
NO...
WHILE HE'S RUNNIN' HE'S HAPPY... IT'S WINNIN' WHAT TAKES THE FUN OUT.
I'LL GIVE THE FREE LICORICE SPEECH OVER HERE.. IS THAT YOUR FAVORITE?
SOAP
YOU BET! I'M A BIG DEVOTED FOLLOWING.
HEY, P.T.!... YOU'RE ACTIN' JES' LIKE RIP VAN WINKLE..
7-24
Mhm?
THE ELECTIONS IS OVER! SAYS SO ON OUR CALENDAR.
My ward!
HARD TO BELIEVE, HUH...? WHATEVER HAPPENED TO ALL THEM WIND-UP CANDIDATES YOU HAD?
WELL, I GUESS some RAN down; SOME ran up the WHITE FLAG and SOME RAN OUT OF FRIENDS!

IT SURE IS FUNNY TO THINK WE GOT A NEW PRESIDENT ALL ELECTED...
WONDER WHO?
GYACK!
7-25

DAGGRABBIT, CHURCHY! I THUNK YOU SEEN A GHOST!
I DID!

C'MON, LET'S RUN UP AN' SEE THE OLD FELLA... I ALLUS HAD A SOFT SPOT IN MY HEART FOR HIM.
THE LAST OF THE RANGE.
7-26

HUH?

TAKE OFF YER HAT.
A GOOD STEER: CHEW the OLD RAG BRAND

KINDA TOO BAD... I WAS HOPIN' THAT WAS THE OL' FELLA... 'STEAD OF A WOODEN SIGN.
YEAH··· ADVERTISIN' CHEWN TOBACCO.
ACK! YOU GOT A WASP ON··· AN' YOU'RE DARN RIGHT! HE COULD OF BEEN ADVERTISIN' SOMETHIN' IMPORTANT TO, SAY, FOREIGN POLICY LIKE···
7-27

IMPORTANT TO FOREIGN POLICY? SUCH AS···?
WELL, LIKE I'VE SAID BEFORE·· CHOCOLATE ICE CREAM···

Chapter 23

DECK US ALL WITH BOSTON CHARLES

12-16
THIRD VERSE! Under Thursday of Crystal Ball MacTruloff Sanity Free Friends' Wens,
MAC?
TRULOFF?
Tuber-Kalosis, Anger cartridge Widow pastry
BROTHER! SOME CAROL!
HOW MANY VERSES, COMPLETE?
JUS' THINKIN' OFF THE TOP OF MY HEAD, I'D SAY TWELVE, ALL TOLD.
ALL?
TOLD?
HOW TOLD?
VERY.
CUT THE BABY TALK OR I WON'T SING NO MORE.
CONGERSMAN, I'M LOOKIN' FOR XMAS CAROLERS...WHERE'S YOUR AIDE, MR. MERELY?
I'M READY... I'M WRITIN' OUT MY SANITY CLAUSE FOR THE PLATFORM ON MY DRUMHEAD...
12-19
THAT'S YOUR SANITY CLAUSE FOR SEEIN' IF THE VOTERS IS IN THEIR RIGHT MINDS WOT YER PLAYIN?
YUP.. AS FOR MERELY, HE'S HIDIN'. SOMEPLACE.
WUMP! WUMP! WUMP!

HE'S AFRAID OF YO' SANITY CLAUSE? OR IS HE AFRAID OF CHRISTMAS?
BOTH.
WUMP WUMP
HE GOT SANITY CLAUSTROPHOBIA.
HIC WUMP WUMP WUMP HOO BOY
WE'LL PRACTICE ON THE WAY TO CAROL REHEARSAL.
"GOOD KING SAUERKRAUT, LOOK OUT! ON YOUR FEETS UNEVEN"
WUMP
12-20
NOW TRY THAT ONE AGAIN 'BOUT THE TWELVE DAYS OF CHRISTMAS.
RIGHT.. I WAS ON THE THIRD VERSE.. Under Thursday of Crispness, MacTruloff sanity Three wench friends
Tu-dors above, An' the parson up a psaltree
THREE WENCH FRIENDS? EITHER YOU GOT THE WORDS UPSIDE DOWN OR MY DRUM'S OUT OF TUNE.
YOU'RE IN A RUT.. THE WRONG GROOVE, YOU'RE A CONSERVATIVE!
PREERP
WOORMP

I BRUNG OVER THE WORDS TO OUR CLASSIC CAROL.
THE TRADITION.
SHOOT.
12-21
Bark us all Bow-wows of Folly, Double-Bubble, Toyland trouble! Woof, Woof, Woof!
Tizzy seas on Melon collie! Dibble-dabble, Scribble-scrabble Goof, Goof, Goof!
I OBJECT! THAT'S A AFFRONT TO OUR GUMMINT.
THERE IS SOMETHIN' WRONG THERE.
IT'S ALL WRONG.. WHO REMEMBERS THE ORIGINAL VERSION?
?
OLD HAGGIS
YEAH..WHO DOES REMEMBER THE ORIGINAL VERSION...ALL FULL OF PEACE AN' LIGHT?
I THINK IT GOES LIKE THIS.. AHEM... ..mi mi DECK..
I GOT IT!.. IT GOES LIKE THIS--TUM TUM
Deck us all with Boston Charlie, Walla Walla Wash., and Kalamazoo! Nora's freezin' on the trolley, Swaller dollar, cauliflour, Alla-garoo!
WUMP! WUMP!
12-22

AAARGH! YOU SUNG THAT A-PURPOSE! TO FRUSTICATE ME! JES' WHEN I WAS THINKIN' OF IT!
ROWR! YOU'RE ALLUS HOGGIN' THE SPOT-LIGHT! YOU CAROL SNATCHER!
THAT'S THE WAY THE PEACE AN' LIGHT VERSION GOES?
AYE... 'PARENTLY.
WHAT'S THE SECOND VERSE?
AS YOU CAN SEE, USUALLY WE DON'T GIT THAT FAR.
LET'S ALL GO SLIDE DOWN A CHIMNEY INTO BED.
HO HUM

MERRY CHRISTMAS.. THIS TIME I WAS WAITIN' FOR YOU..
12-25
EVERY CHRISTMAS MORNIN' YOU COMES OVER.. FIRST ONE.. ALLUS BRINGS ME A FLOWER WHAT YOU SAVED FROM OUR SUMMER.
HUMPH
IT DON'T INDICATE NOTHIN'.. I ALLUS GITS UP AFORE DAWN 'CAUSE, BY GEORGE Y. WELLS, IT TAKES A LONG TIME FOR A PORKYPINE TO GIT HIS PAJAMAS OFF.
HERE! I FORGIT HOW I HAPPENS TO BE CARRYIN' THIS... IT DON'T MEAN A THING..... Y'GOT A SPOON? EATIN' FRIED EGGS WITH A FORK TAKES A COLLEGE EDUCATION, SON.
YOU NEVER FORGITS.
THERE'S NOTHING LIKE A NEW-PAINTED MORNING, POGO.

THE NEWS